THE TRIAL OF
JOE HARLAN JUNIOR

J.K. FRANKO

TALION PUBLISHING

Published in the United Kingdom and the rest of the world by Talion
Publishing

Cambridge, UK

A catalogue record for this book is available from the
British Library

ISBN 978-1999318833

For my wife, Raquel.
I love you more every day.

This is an adaptation from the play of the same name which was performed in Covent Garden, London on April 6, 2019 — the evening of the launch of the first installment of the Talion Series, *Eye for Eye*.

The Trial of Joe Harlan is the prequel to the Talion Series.

Winds in the east, mist comin' in
Like something is brewin' about to begin
Can't put me finger on what lies in store
But I feel what's to happen, all happened before

Mary Poppins, by Don DaGradi

Austin, Texas
July 11, 2016

Kristy Wise jerked awake.

At least, she thought she was awake.

She was confused. It felt like her eyes were open, but she couldn't see anything. She had no idea where she was. She tried to sit up, but nothing happened. A wave of fear crashed against her as she tried to move her legs and they refused to respond.

I'm paralyzed! He paralyzed me!

Her heart rate spiked and her mind raced as she tried to recall something, anything that would help her understand where she was or what was happening. But in the pitch black, there was nothing. No audio cues, no visual cues, just palpable emptiness.

Oh God, I'm dead! He killed me. I'm dead!

Then she noticed a faint smell. Familiar. Sweet. Too sweet, making her want to retch. She tried to breathe, tried to suck in fresh air, but nothing came. Nothing. It was as if she was sucking on a tube that was sealed at the other end.

That's when the panic set in.

She opened her mouth to scream but realized to her horror that she couldn't. The trapdoor to her lungs was sealed shut.

It's a nightmare. It's just a nightmare. You're asleep. Just wake up! Wake up!

As she fought to wake up, she felt herself drifting.

Falling? No, sinking—into something dense. She felt increasing pressure. As if the weight of an entire ocean was slowly crushing her body.

She struggled, her heart machine-gunning as it fought to oxygenate her blood, to feed her starving organs.

Her chest was screaming. Burning.

She wanted air.

She needed air.

And that was when she heard them.

Three gunshots.

Ptaff   Ptaff   Ptaff

Kristy bolted upright, gasping, spluttering and sucking in air.

Cool, clean air.

Her bedsheets were drenched with sweat. The t-shirt she'd slept in was stuck to her body.

It was dark, but for a shard of moonlight that cut across her bedroom slicing her bed in half. It was deathly quiet. Not a sound, except the monotonous white haw of the A/C.

The clock on her nightstand read 4:00 a.m.

The day had finally come. After so many months. It was time to face it.

To face him.

She had optimistically set her alarm for 6:30 a.m. in hopes of getting a full nine hours. But that was just wishful thinking. She'd slept fitfully again that night, as she had for many months. Ever since it happened.

She hadn't had this particular nightmare in a while, but her dreams were always haunted by shadows. Foreboding.

Premonitions of something to come?

She knew they weren't real. She didn't fear them. She wasn't afraid to go to sleep. She just hated the fact that she never felt rested.

This nightmare was the worst one, because there was nothing she could do. There was no one there. No *thing* attacking her. Just paralysis. Sinking. And then the three gunshots.

Kristy sighed and swung her legs out of bed. She knew she couldn't sleep anymore. She got dressed for a run, and quietly made her way downstairs.

As she turned at the landing on the staircase, she could see warm light coming from the first floor of her house. She could hear whispered voices.

"Mornin' angel," Deb Wise said to her daughter as she appeared in the kitchen.

"Morning."

Kristy's father, Tom Wise, was seated at the island in front of a coffee cup.

"What're you guys doing up so early?" Kristy asked.

"Couldn't sleep," Tom answered.

Deb walked across the kitchen and gave her daughter a big, enveloping hug.

"You're dressed for exercise," she said, stepping back.

Kristy nodded. "I couldn't sleep either. Wanna clear my head, you know?"

"It's still dark out," Tom said, looking out the window.

"I'm gonna drive down to the lake, run there."

Town Lake was a seven-minute drive from the Wise's home. It was a popular and populated running trail, even in the early morning.

"You be careful, then. You got your lights?" Deb asked.

Kristy nodded. She walked over and gave her dad a hug from behind and a kiss on the cheek. "See y'all in a bit."

* * *

After her run, Kristy took a hot shower. When she'd finished, she stood under the showerhead and turned the water slowly from hot to cold. She stayed under the ice-cold water, letting it run down her hair and along her back. She wanted to feel it, to be invigorated by it. To feel... clean.

She was a mess. She knew that.

She wanted... no, she *needed* it all to be over. She hated the fact that something that she couldn't even remember had become such a big part of her life. There was a small part of her that wished it had all been buried, swept under the rug. Undiscovered. It was frustrating. Infuriating.

Still, she wanted Harlan to pay.

She'd put up with all of it—the investigation, the trial preparation, the media, sitting out a semester of college—the whole mess, because she wanted justice. He needed to be punished. He should never be allowed to do this to anyone again, ever.

She dressed for trial in clothing the prosecutor, Abigail Kraft, had recommended.

Business clothes. Comfortable. Navy blue skirt and jacket. Pale blue blouse. Dark blue pumps.

Her trial uniform.

They'd spent most of the previous Thursday going over her and her roommate Bethany Rosen's testimony and preparing for the trial.

As the prep session progressed, Kristy was impressed at how Kraft was able to pull together a compelling story about what happened that Halloween night using the little that Kristy could remember and what Bethany had seen. It was powerful stuff.

Harlan didn't stand a chance.

Kristy left the session feeling confident. They had a solid case. And she knew Harlan—not well, but enough to know that he wouldn't do well on the stand.

They're going to hate him she thought as she touched up her hair, pulling a few strands loose.

She checked the time.

7:15 a.m.

They were due at the courthouse at 8:30 a.m. But they—she, her parents, the prosecutor—had agreed to meet earlier to try and avoid the press that was likely to be there.

Downstairs, her parents were already waiting in the living room. Her father was pacing slowly, dressed in a dark grey suit, white shirt, and a somber tie. Her mother was in a light grey outfit.

"We look like a bunch of depressed accountants," Kristy quipped as she entered the room, trying to lighten the mood.

Tom Wise smiled, but only with his mouth. His eyes betrayed what he was feeling.

Her mother turned and smiled reassuringly at her. "You look good, girl," she said, walking over to her. Then added, "Let me... " as she carefully rearranged the few loose strands of her daughter's hair. The act was intimate. Maternal.

Then without turning, she said, "Come on, Tom. Let's get going."

* * *

The three rode to the courthouse in silence. The streets and the sky wore matching slate grey, reflecting the mood of the Audi's occupants. The only touch of color was the streetlights that reflected off the drizzle on the wet pavement.

"I'm going to drop you off by the entrance, then park," Tom said as he turned onto Guadalupe Street.

They were early, but Kristy spotted Abigail Kraft standing outside the courthouse door alone. Kraft had called Kristy the night before to confirm that she'd spoken with the judge and had arranged for them to be admitted into the building early.

"There she is," Kristy said, pointing.

Tom pulled up and let his wife and daughter out of the car.

"Good morning," Kraft said, giving each of the women a quick embrace. "Come on. Let's get inside. We can talk then."

The three quickly made their way into the building and through the security checkpoint and the metal detector.

* * *

Kristy and her mother took their seats in the courtroom gallery, right behind the table where the prosecution would be seated—the table closest to the jury and furthest from the courtroom door.

They had the courtroom to themselves. Still, they spoke in whispers.

"How're you feeling?" Kraft asked.

"I'm good. Ready for this to be over," Kristy replied, noticing that Kraft's hair was slightly damp from the precipitation outside.

"Well, don't worry. You're ready. You look very nice, by the way. Very appropriate." Kraft made a face, not pleased with her choice of words. "You look exactly right," she amended.

"Thanks," Kristy replied with a nervous smile

"I'm going to get organized. But, if you have any questions, I'm right here." Kraft turned to the table and the topmost of three boxes stacked next to it. She opened the box and began to remove notebooks and documents.

Five minutes later, Kraft's paralegal, Jodie Moon, arrived and helped.

Deb looked at her daughter and smiled while gently squeezing her hand.

At 8:00, Tom entered the courtroom and took a seat next to his wife.

A few minutes later, Brandon Fletcher, the attorney for the defendant, arrived with another lawyer from his firm and a female paralegal. They began the same unpacking ritual at their table.

At 8:15, Bethany arrived and took a seat next to Kristy, sandwiching her in with her mother. Tom Wise sat at the end of the row by the wall.

Kristy noticed the bailiff speaking to the two attorneys in hushed tones. Then Kraft approached.

"The judge is running late this morning. Flat tire. But we should start up at about eight-forty-five."

"Restroom?" Bethany asked.

"Sure," Kraft replied. "I'll show you."

When Bethany stood, Kristy rose with her and nodded to her mother. Bethany and Kristy followed Kraft out the courtroom door. It was clear that the courthouse was open for business.

To Kristy, it all felt unreal. Like a movie set. Not her life.

There was a line of people waiting outside the courtroom. Another burly bailiff stood guard.

"Courtroom opens to the public at eight thirty," Kraft said, noticing the two girls looking at the line. She walked them down the hall and around a corner, then pointed, "Down at the end, on the left."

Bethany and Kristy, aware of the other women in the bathroom, kept their conversation to a minimum and in hushed tones.

"You ready for this?"

Kristy nodded, sighing, "I just want it to be over."

"Over and for that bastard to get locked up," Bethany said.

"Yeah."

"Hey... It's come to Jesus time, Kris. And he's going to pay," Bethany said, with fire in her eyes, "one way or another."

Kristy half smiled and shrugged.

Bethany gave Kristy a hug, and as she did, said to her, "Come on. Let's put this asshole away."

* * *

When the girls returned to the courtroom, everyone had taken their places. The public had been let in, and the gallery was full.

As they walked back to their seats, they passed the defense table, where Brandon Fletcher was seated next to Joe Harlan Junior.

* * *

The following is a transcript of the proceedings as they unfolded.

To watch a live performance of the trial, filmed in London's Covent Garden, and to deliver your own verdict, go to

www.jkfranko.com/thetrial

then resume reading at page 50

IN THE DISTRICT COURT

250TH JUDICIAL DISTRICT

TRAVIS COUNTY TEXAS

```
-------------------------- )
                           )
                           )
THE STATE OF TEXAS         )
                           )  Cause No.
v.                         )  15-04081971
                           )
JOSEPH ALAN HARLAN JUNIOR  )
                           )
-------------------------- )
```

JURY TRIAL
July 12, 2016

BEFORE THE HONORABLE DAVID MORALES

APPEARANCES:

> **Ms. Abigail Kraft**
> Assistant District Attorney
> Appearing on behalf of the State of
> Texas

> **Mr. Brandon Fletcher**
> Goodwin, Fletcher & Rodriguez
> Appearing on behalf of the Defendant,
> Joseph Alan Harlan Junior

(On the record)

Bailiff: All Rise. The Honorable David Morales
           presiding.

(Jury enters and take their seats)

Judge: Please be seated. At this time the Court calls Cause Number 15-04081971, The State of Texas versus Joseph Alan Harlan Jr. Will the parties please enter their appearances and announce for the record?

Prosecution: (Rises) Abigail Kraft appearing on behalf of the State of Texas. The State is ready for trial your honor.

Defense: (Rises) Brandon Fletcher appearing on behalf of the Defendant. We are ready to proceed.

Judge: Very good. Will the jury please stand? Please raise your right hands. In response to the following oath, please respond "I do."

           "You and each of you do solemnly swear that in the case of the State of Texas against the defendant, Joseph Alan Harlan Jr., you will a true verdict render according to the law and the evidence, so help you God."

(Jury assents)

           Please be seated. Very well. The case will proceed as follows. Each party will have fifteen minutes for their opening statements. After that, the State will present its case. Once the State rests, the Defendant will present his case. We will then hear closing arguments from each side, after which the jury will be excused for deliberations.

Any questions?

Defense: (Inaudible) ...and upholding the
             letter of the law at the prosecutor's
             office then?

Prosecution: Some of us believe in what we do.
             We don't work for the headlines.

Judge: Counselors I asked if there are any
             questions.

Prosecution: No questions, your honor.

Defense: None, Judge.

Judge: Is there something you'd like to
             share with the court, counselor?

Defense: Um, no, your honor. Just, um, the
             prosecutor and I, um, we have
             history.

Judge: Congratulations, Mr. Fletcher. But,
             the next time I ask a question and
             you're not paying attention, I'll find
             you in contempt and you'll be history
             in my court. Is that clear, sir?

Defense: Yes, your honor.

Judge: Very well. So, if neither of you have
             any questions for me, then I suggest
             that you begin, Ms. Kraft.

Prosecution: (Rises) Thank you, your honor.

             Ladies and Gentlemen of the jury,
             I'll be brief, because this is a
             simple case. My name is Abigail

Kraft. And I represent the State
of Texas in this case against the
Defendant, Joseph Alan Harlan, Jr.

Halloween can be a night of fun,
trick-or-treating, costumes, and
parties. But, for Kristy Wise,
Halloween truly became a night of
horror. The evidence will show that,
like many other college students, her
night began with dress-up, fun, and
laughter. But it ended in a hospital
bed, fighting off a near-fatal
overdose of Rohypnol — the date rape
drug — after having been raped by the
Defendant, Joseph Alan Harlan, Jr.

The prosecution will present evidence
that will show, beyond a reasonable
doubt, that Joseph Alan Harlan, Jr.
stalked and then drugged Kristy Wise
with the sole intention of having
sex with her without her consent.
And, that when he was quite literally
caught in the act of this offense by
Kristy's roommate, he fled the scene
of the crime, leaving his victim
naked and unconscious.

Thank you.

(The Prosecution is seated)

Defense: (Rises) Ladies and gentlemen. My name
           is Brandon Fletcher, and I represent
           Joe Harlan.

           The prosecution has just claimed
           to have evidence proving beyond a
           reasonable doubt that my client

raped Kristy Wise. That he willfully stalked Kristy Wise and then drugged her with the sole intent of having his wicked way with her.

I, on the other hand, will present and prove to you the reality. The truth. And the truth is that, as can happen with two young adults, Joe and Kristy Wise met at a Halloween party. They had a few drinks. Maybe even a few too many. And that Kristy Wise invited Joe back to her apartment where they both, as two consenting adults, had sex.

In fact, you will hear — from Kristy — in her own words — you'll hear her recount how she planned to have relations that night with Joe and how she planned on rewarding him, as her prince for the evening.

This is not a rape case. And the evidence you will hear today will prove it.

Thank you.

(The Defense is seated)

Judge: Ms. Kraft, please call your first witness.

Prosecution: The State calls Bethany Rosen to the stand.

(Bethany Rosen takes the stand)

Judge: Miss Rosen, do you swear that the

testimony you are about to give
will be truth, the whole truth, and
nothing but the truth, so help you
God?

Rosen: I do.

Prosecution: Please state your name.

Rosen: Bethany Rosen.

Prosecution: Where do you reside?

Rosen: 2300 Nueces Street, Apartment 240,
           Austin, TX 78705.

Prosecution: What is your occupation?

Rosen: I am a student... at the University
           of Texas. A sophomore. I'm studying
           psychology.

Prosecution: Bethany, do you know the victim,
              Kristy Wise?

Rosen: I do.

Prosecution: Can you tell us how?

Rosen: We're friends. I first met Kristy
           when I started high school, at
           Westlake High. We'd just moved to
           Austin, so I was the new girl. Well
           — one of the new girls. Kristy and I
           got assigned to be lab partners... in
           biology.

           Later, after high school, we both got
           into UT Austin, so we decided to room
           together.

Prosecution: So, you are roommates at the address on Nueces Street?

Rosen: Yes ma'am, we are. Well, we were until a few months ago.

Prosecution: And do you know the Defendant, Joe Harlan Junior?

Rosen: I do.

Prosecution: Can you tell us how?

Rosen: I met him at school — at UT. We know some of the same people. So, we would see each other from time to time, you know, around campus. And at parties.

Prosecution: How would you describe your relationship with him?

Rosen: My relationship with him? None. I mean, I knew who he was. I assume he knew who I was. And we'd say hi occasionally, but nothing more. We were... acquaintances, I guess? If you want to put a label on it.

Prosecution: Did you ever discuss him with Kristy — you guys ever talk about him?

Rosen: Yeah. We thought —

Defense: (Stands) Objection, your honor, hearsay.

Judge: Sustained. Miss Rosen, you can testify as to what you thought, but not as to anything that Miss Wise told you. She'll have her turn to speak for herself. Please rephrase your question Ms. Kraft.

Prosecution: Bethany, what did you think of Joe Harlan?

Rosen: I thought he was kind of full of himself. His dad is a politician — a state senator. And he's always talking about him. But — I mean — I get that, it's cool to be proud of your parents and all. But with Joe, it was always like he was trying to show off. Name dropping, you know.

But... besides that, he's also... kind of creepy. You know, flirting with everyone. Eyes all over you. You know, with him you were always like... dude, hello, my eyes are up here.

And the guys he hangs around with aren't much better. I mean, some are nice, but the others are kind of shady. Do you know what I mean?

Prosecution: Can you tell us about Halloween night?

Rosen: Sure. So, Kristy and I went out for the night, you know. It's really a big night on campus. We dressed up like Mario and Luigi.

You know, from the video game... the Mario Brothers. I was Luigi.

I've got photos on my phone if you wanna see em'.

Prosecution: No. That won't be necessary. Can you tell us about the night?

Rosen: Yeah so... Kristy's not real big on going out. She had a big term paper she was working on that was due right after Thanksgiving. And she didn't want to take it with her on break. So, she was planning to stay home. That's why I did the Mario Brothers costume. I figured if I got costumes for both of us, I could convince her.

I mean, who's Luigi without Mario, right?

Prosecution: So, when Halloween night came around, it wasn't Kristy's plan to go out?

Rosen: No, she wanted to stay home and study.

Prosecution: Okay, then what happened?

Rosen: Well, if she'd done what she wanted, none of this probably would have happened. But, I convinced her we should go... Oh God... sorry. I mean...

Prosecution: Are you alright? Do you need a moment?

Rosen: Sorry. No. I'm fine.

So, I convinced her to go out.

We headed out at around eight o'clock. A friend of mine — of ours — was having a party at her house. Her name's Lara. Lara Ashton. Anyway, so we headed over to her house. It's only about a fifteen minute walk from our apartment.

Prosecution: Were there a lot of people there?

Rosen: Yeah. The place was jumping. We were having a good time. And then Joe showed up with his pals, Frank and Marty and a couple of other guys I didn't know.

Prosecution: And when you say Frank and Marty. Who are these individuals?

Rosen: Stern. Frank Stern, He's one of the shady guys I mentioned before. It was him and Marty McCall. They were all roommates.

So, we were all just kind of chillin' and stuff, and I start to look around and I don't see Kristy. But, you know, Lara's boyfriend, Jimmy, was grilling outside, we were all kind of in and out. So, at first, I didn't think much of it. But then I started looking around for her and couldn't find her.

Prosecution: And what time is this?

Rosen: Um, I'd say around 10:30. So, I get my phone out to text her and that's when I see the Tweets.

Prosecution: Which Tweets?

Rosen: Um, so two Tweets from Bunny Ears, that's Kristy's handle. Then, just as I'm about to send her a message, the third one comes through.

Prosecution: May I approach the witness, your Honor?

Judge: You may.

Prosecution: Let me hand you what I have marked as State's Exhibits 1, 2, and 3. Have you seen these before, Bethany?

Rosen: Those are the Tweets.

Prosecution: Could you read them out loud please, with the timestamps?

Rosen: 10:22 p.m. Feeling better. Love Halloween. Be safe everyone!

10:24 p.m. Found someone special. Chivalry is not dead! Gonna get Funky tonight!

10:31 p.m. Reward your prince charming. Life is short.

Prosecution: What did you think when you first saw these Tweets?

Rosen: That's not Kristy.

Prosecution: Why did you think that?

Rosen: Well, first off, Kristy's super-private. She never Tweets. I mean, she has a Twitter account, but she only has like seven followers — including me. And she would never use the word "funky." Ever.

Prosecution: So, what did you do?

Rosen: Well, I was weirded out, so I started looking for her. I thought it might be a joke or something — someone had taken her phone maybe. And that's when Marty, Joe's friend, told me what happened. He said that she was outside, in back by the grill, but that she started feeling kind of woozy. So, Joe — him (Indicating the Defendant) — he offered to walk her home.

And that's when I started to freak.

Prosecution: Why did you start to freak?

Rosen: I don't know. Intuition, I guess? All the weird Tweets and that "prince charming" crap — sorry, your honor. Then I find out she's left the party with Joe Momma.

Prosecution: Joe who?

Rosen: Joe Momma. That's what we call him.

Defense: (Stands) Objection your Honor, the name-calling is unnecessary, inappropriate and irrelevant.

Prosecution: Your honor, if I may. I don't believe the witness is name-calling. It speaks to state of mind.

Judge: Okay counselor, you can follow up,
              but be very careful.

Prosecution: Yes, your honor. Bethany — you
              just referred to the Defendant as Joe
              Momma. Can you explain why?

Rosen: Well, like I said before, Joe always
              gave off this kind of creepy vibe.
              So, I came up with this joke name for
              him from an old "Yo Momma" joke.

              The joke was "Yo momma is so dumb she
              failed a blood test." We thought that
              if he had his blood tested, he'd fail
              — you know, like for STD's — so we
              called him —

Defense: Objection your honor, that's hearsay.

Prosecution: Your honor, we're not offering
              the testimony to prove that the
              Defendant would actually fail a blood
              test, it goes to the state of mind
              of the witness and the victim. How
              they perceived him. If they called
              him that, it begs the question
              whether Miss Wise would want to have
              intercourse with him.

Judge: I'll allow it.

Rosen: So, yeah, we called him Joe Momma.

Prosecution: Joe Momma. Okay, so you are at the
              party. You're concerned that she's
              gone. What did you do then?

Rosen: I called her. She didn't answer.

Prosecution: At what time?

Rosen: According to my phone, it was 10:42
            p.m. — so just minutes after she
            sent the "prince charming" Tweet. No
            answer. So, I left the party and went
            back to our apartment. Like I said,
            it's about a fifteen-minute walk.

            When I got there, I went straight up
            to our unit.

Prosecution: And what happened?

Rosen: I opened the door, and there he was,
            right there in the middle of the
            living room, on the floor. He was
            lying on top of her. I guess he heard
            the door, because as I came in, he
            was rolling off of her. He had his
            pants down around his ankles. And I
            saw he was still — you know — erect —
            with a condom on. But she was out of
            it. Completely.

Prosecution: How do you mean?

Rosen: I mean, she wasn't moving. She was
            just lying there. Her top was kind
            of open, and she was naked from the
            waist down.

Prosecution: What did you do?

Rosen: Oh, I freaked. I pulled out my pepper
            spray. And I told him to get the...
            I used really vulgar language, your
            honor. I told him to get the "F" off
            of her, telling him to get out.

I was yelling. I don't remember everything I said. But I was calling him names and just telling him to get out. And he was scared. He looked guilty...

Defense: Objection, your honor. Calls for speculation.

Prosecution: Your honor, the witness is giving her impressions of what she saw. We can all register and interpret human emotion and reaction.

Judge: I'll allow it. Continue Miss Rosen.

Rosen: Sorry — I don't remember the question.

Prosecution: You were telling us about going back to your apartment, and what you saw.

Rosen: Oh, right. So, yeah. I started yelling. And Joe got up and he was pulling his pants up with one hand and holding the other one out at me like to keep me away. And he kept saying, "She's fine. She's fine."

But she didn't look fine. She was just finished having sex — on the floor — in the living room — and she wasn't moving. That's not fine.

Then, I guess he left, because I was alone with her. And I tried to wake her up, but she wouldn't — she didn't respond. So, I called 911 and they sent an ambulance for her.

But they wouldn't let me ride with her.

Prosecution: So, what did you do?

Rosen: The only thing I could do. I called her mom and told her what happened.

Prosecution: Bethany, did Kristy ever tell you that she was attracted to Joe?

Rosen: God, no!

Defense: Object... Never mind.

Prosecution: You know Kristy well. She's your close friend. Do you think she had sex with Mr. Harlan of her own free will?

Defense: Objection your honor. Calls for speculation.

Prosecution: Your honor, the witness —

Judge: Sustained. You know better than that Ms. Kraft. Try another line of questioning.

Prosecution: That's all I have your honor. I pass the witness.

(Prosecutor sits)

(Counsel for the Defense stands)

Defense: Hello Miss Rosen. My name is Brandon Fletcher. I just have a few questions for you.

Rosen: Okay.

Defense: You were not with Kristy when the
            text messages were sent from her
            Twitter account, correct?

Rosen: That's correct.

Defense: So, you have no first-hand knowledge
            as to whether she sent them or not?

Rosen: Well, I know —

Defense: Objection. Non-responsive.

Judge: Sustained. Miss Rosen, I'm afraid
            it's a yes or no question. You just
            need to answer the question you're
            asked.

Rosen: Yes Judge, your honor.

Defense: Again, you were not with Kristy when
            the text messages were sent from her
            Twitter account, correct?

Rosen: Correct.

Defense: So, you have no first-hand knowledge
            as to whether she sent them or not.
            Is that correct?

Rosen: Yes.

Defense: What did you have to drink — on
            Halloween night?

Rosen: Before or after Joe raped Kristy?

Defense: Objection your honor...

Judge: Counselor, I'm afraid your question was not clear about timing.

Defense: Apologies, your honor. Miss Rosen, prior to returning to your apartment on Halloween night, what did you have to drink?

Rosen: Vodka.

Defense: How many?

Rosen: Three or four.

Defense: Was it three or four?

Rosen: I don't remember exactly.

Defense: Were you drinking straight vodka, or vodka and tonic, or...

Rosen: Straight vodka. You know... Calories...

Defense: What did Miss Wise have to drink?

Rosen: You mean besides the roofies they slipped her?

Defense: Actually, let's discuss that, since you brought it up. After Miss Wise was taken to the clinic —

Rosen: Hospital...

Defense: Yes — after she was taken to the hospital, she was found to have drugs in her system, is that correct?

Rosen: Yes. Rohypnol, which is a date-rape
            drug.

Defense: Do you know how that drug... or
            more specifically, do you know first-
            hand — how that drug got into her
            system?

Rosen: No.

Defense: So, to be clear, you are not here
            to testify that Joe gave Kristy
            Rohypnol, are you?

Rosen: No, but it's very —

Defense: Objection, your honor...

Judge: Sustained. Miss Rosen, you'll be
            able to clarify if the prosecution
            chooses to ask you more questions in
            a moment. For now, please just answer
            the questions you're asked.

Rosen: Okay, but I don't like the way this
            works, judge. No offense.

Defense: So, to be clear, you did not see, nor
            can you testify, that Joe gave Kristy
            Rohypnol. Correct?

Rosen: Correct.

Defense: And, likewise, you cannot testify,
            you have no evidence, that Joe knew
            that Kristy had even ingested any
            drugs, is that correct?

Rosen: Yes, it is.

Defense: In fact, you didn't even know that Kristy Wise had ingested any drugs until you learned that from the lab results, is this also correct?

Rosen: Yes.

Defense: And, in addition, you are not here to testify today as to what Joe Harlan knows, is that right?

Rosen: About what?

Defense: Precisely. You don't know, you can't possibly know, what Joe Harlan knows or doesn't know, correct?

Rosen: I'm sorry. I'm confused. About what?

Defense: For example, does my client, Joe Harlan, know how many vodkas you drank on Halloween?

Rosen: I haven't got a clue.

Defense: And, likewise, you have no clue, no idea whether Mr. Harlan had any knowledge of the fact that Kristy had ingested any drugs on Halloween, correct?

Rosen: He knew that —

Defense: Objection your honor. Responsiveness.

Prosecution: (Stands) Objection. Your honor, Counselor is badgering the witness. He just asked Miss Rosen about what Mr. Harlan knew, and she began to answer the question by stating – "He knew that..." and then he cut Bethany off...

Judge: Objection overruled, Mr. Fletcher. Please let the witness answer — or at least get to something objectionable before you object. You chose the phrasing of your question. You've got to live with it.

Prosecution: Your honor, you haven't ruled on my objection.

Judge: What did it sound like, Madame Prosecutor? The Defendant's objection is overruled. The State's objection is sustained. Please answer the question, Miss Rosen.

Rosen: Thank you, your honor. As I was saying, he knew that Kristy was feeling unwell - bad enough that she wanted to go home. If she was feeling unwell, sex would be the farthest thing from her mind.

Defense: I have nothing further for this witness, your honor.

(Counsel for the Defense retakes his seat)

Prosecution: (Stands) The state calls Joe Harlan to the stand.

(Bethany Rosen steps down)

(Joe Harlan Junior takes the stand)

Judge: Do you swear that the testimony you are about to give will be truth, the whole truth, and nothing but the truth, so help you God?

Harlan: I do.

Prosecution: Please state your name.

Harlan: Joseph Harlan Junior.

Prosecution: Mr. Harlan, you understand that you are accused of the rape of Kristy Wise?

Harlan: I do.

Prosecution: Okay. So, first, let's get some basic facts out of the way.

Harlan: Okay.

Prosecution: Is it true that on Halloween night you were at the same party as Kristy Wise?

Harlan: Yes.

Prosecution: And prior to that point, you had never dated Kristy, is that correct?

Harlan: It is.

Prosecution: Never had lunch together?

Harlan: No.

Prosecution: Never been to the movies?

Harlan: No.

Prosecution: What was the longest amount of

time you had spent alone with Kristy Wise, prior to Halloween night?

Harlan: Um... alone?

Prosecution: Yes, Mr. Harlan. Alone.

Harlan: We'd never been alone.

Prosecution: No? Never held her hand?

Harlan: No.

Prosecution: Met her parents?

Harlan: No.

Prosecution: Studied together?

Harlan: No.

Prosecution: Had a one-on-one conversation? Face-to-face?

Harlan: No.

Prosecution: How about a phone call?

Harlan: No.

Prosecution: Is it fair to say that, prior to Halloween night, Kristy was nothing more than a mere acquaintance to you?

Harlan: Yes.

Prosecution: And you don't deny that you knew she was feeling ill that night, do you?

Harlan: No.

Prosecution: In fact, you volunteered to walk her home, didn't you, after she complained about feeling unwell?

Defense: Objection your honor. Is the prosecutor asking questions or testifying?

Judge: Overruled.

Prosecution: Mr. Harlan, did you offer to take Kristy Wise home from the party you both attended on Halloween night?

Harlan: I did.

Prosecution: You walked her back to her apartment, correct?

Harlan: That is correct.

Prosecution: How did Kristy appear to you, when you walked her home?

Harlan: How did she appear?

Prosecution: How unwell did she look?

Harlan: She looked fine. I guess. A bit tired maybe, but fine.

Prosecution: Did you give her date rape drugs?

Harlan: No ma'am. I did not.

Prosecution: Well, if you didn't, that would mean that she would have to have ingested them at the party. Sometime before she started feeling unwell. Do you agree?

Harlan: Or later, I guess?

Prosecution: Later? Wait, are you testifying that you believe that Kristy Wise took Rohypnol on her own? That she administered it to herself, knowingly, after the party? After you walked her home?

Harlan: I don't know. I didn't see her take anything.

Prosecution: Right. So, you do agree with me, then, that she must have ingested those drugs prior to leaving the party?

Defense: (Stands) Objection your honor. The witness has already —

Judge: Overruled.

Prosecution: Please answer the question. Do you agree with me that she had to have ingested those drugs prior to leaving the party?

Harlan: That sounds logical.

Prosecution: Is that a "yes?"

Harlan: Yes, ma'am. Yes. I agree.

Prosecution: Then, it's also logical that, while you were walking her home, the drugs were spreading through her system, taking their effect.

Defense: Objection, your honor. Does the
             prosecution actually have any
             questions for my client, or would she
             rather continue testifying on his
             behalf?

Judge: Overruled.

Prosecution: Here's a question. Mr. Harlan,
             do you know how long it takes for
             Rohypnol to take effect?

Harlan: No.

Prosecution: Would you disagree that the drug
             takes effect 15 to 20 minutes after
             administration?

Defense: Objection, your honor. My client is
             not a medical professional.

Judge: Overruled. Just because he isn't a
             medical professional, it doesn't
             mean he wouldn't know the answer.
             We've all heard of Google, Mr.
             Fletcher.

Prosecution: Mr. Harlan. You don't disagree?

Harlan: I... I don't know.

Prosecution: Okay. So now. Mr. Harlan, here's
             an interesting question. How long did
             it take for you to get from the party
             to Kristy's apartment?

Harlan: About twenty minutes.

Prosecution: Okay, and you've already agreed
             with me that she had to have ingested

the Rohypnol while at the party,
correct?

Harlan: Yes. Go on.

Prosecution: Go on...? So, you do follow the
logic, then? By the time you reached
Kristy's apartment, she would have
been completely under the effects of
the drug, correct?

Harlan: I guess.

Prosecution: So then, please tell the jury,
in your own words, how Kristy looked
when you got to her apartment.

Defense: Objection, your honor. The
prosecution seems to be going
around in circles. She must clearly
think that if she asks my client the
same question over and over, she
might eventually get the answer she
wants.

Judge: Overruled. The witness may answer the
question.

Defense: Your honor —

Judge: Overruled counselor. You may answer
the question, Mr. Harlan, but before
you do — Ms. Kraft, get to the point.
I can feel myself growing old up
here.

Prosecution: Yes, your honor. Mr. Harlan,
please tell the jury how Kristy
looked when you got to her apartment.

Harlan: As I said... she looked fine.

Prosecution: Was she slurring?

Harlan: No.

Prosecution: Was she lucid?

Harlan: Yes.

Prosecution: Mr. Harlan, are you aware of the effects of Rohypnol?

Harlan: No ma'am.

Prosecution: Would you be surprised to learn that they include: drowsiness, sleep, dizziness, loss of motor control, decreased reaction time, impaired judgement, lack of coordination, slurred speech, confusion, and amnesia?

Harlan: If you say so, ma'am.

Prosecution: But you claim that when you got back to her apartment, Kristy "looked fine"?

Harlan: Yes ma'am.

Prosecution: Mr. Harlan. You're not here to tell us that the lab that tested Kristy's blood was wrong, and that there were no drugs in her system, are you?

Harlan: Um... No.

Prosecution: Ok. Just a few more questions.

Did you see Kristy using her phone to send the Tweets that her friend, Bethany, read out earlier?

Harlan: No. But then I was in the bathroom for a bit. I assume she posted them while I was in there.

Prosecution: Oh, right. So, you just walked a girl home, and I guess that walk must have gone really well because, according to you, Kristy took the earliest opportunity to post those Tweets as soon as she got back to her apartment, right?

Harlan: We had a nice talk.

Prosecution: And things were going really well. Right?

Harlan: Yes.

Prosecution: So well that you decide to lock yourself in the bathroom for ten minutes?

Harlan: Well, Ma'am. When you gotta go, you gotta go.

Prosecution: (Nods)

Does it seem odd to you that there were no fingerprints found on Kristy's phone? She sent all these Tweets, but her phone didn't have her fingerprints on it. Odd. Don't you think?

Harlan: Maybe she wiped it down.

Prosecution: Before deciding that she wanted to
have sex with you?

Harlan: I guess.

Prosecution: I'm through with this witness,
your honor.

(The Prosecution retakes her seat)

Judge: Counselor.

Defense: (Stands) Hi Joe. You alright?

Harlan: Fine sir, thank you.

Defense: I really just have a couple of
questions for you. Joe. How do you
feel about Kristy Wise?

Harlan: I think she's amazing. She's a great
person. We didn't really manage to
spend much time alone together before
Halloween, but I'd been around her
in group settings, and she's just a
great...

Defense: Your honor, may I approach the
witness?

Judge: (Nods)

Defense: Are you okay Joe? Would you like some
water?

Harlan: No thanks. I'm okay. I just can't
believe it's come to this.

Defense: Are you okay to continue, Joe?

Harlan: (Nodding) Yes. I'm good. I'm fine.
Um, like I was saying, she's a great
person. And I really thought this was
going to turn into something more,
you know, something special. I mean,
we had a great time talking, and
getting to know each other. She's got
a great sense of humor. And she's
really smart. But... well... It's all
just so messed up now.

Defense: Joe, would you ever do anything to
hurt Kristy?

Harlan: No. Never. I swear. I would never do
anything to hurt her.

Defense: And Joe, when you went out on
Halloween, did you have anything to
drink?

Harlan: Sure, it was Halloween. Marty was
designated driver. So, yeah. I did
some shots. Tequila. Maybe one too
many, but everyone was drinking.

Defense: Do you feel you were impaired?

Harlan: Well, I wouldn't have driven, but
no, I was good. I remember the whole
night. I remember everything.

Defense: Now, Joe. It's been established
that you had relations that night,
on Halloween. Did Kristy consent to
that?

Harlan: Absolutely. In fact, she was the one
that wanted to use the condom, which,
you know, was cool with me.

Defense: And when you finished, what happened?

Harlan: We kind of fell asleep on the floor. You know... as we were. Next thing I know, her roommate bursts into the room and starts yelling and screaming and swearing. Accusing me of all sorts of stuff. I got scared and left.

Defense: Is there anything you want to say to Kristy?

Harlan: Yeah. Absolutely. Listen. I don't know how things got so messed up. And I don't know who gave you the drugs. I really don't. But I want you to know I would never do that. I could never do that. And I'm sorry, I'm really sorry it's come to this. But, in all honesty, I really thought... we had something special. And truly... I... from the bottom of my heart, I believe that we were both consenting that night. I would never have forced myself on you. I would never force myself on anyone, and I'm sorry, so sorry, that you would even think I could do that. And I hope — I really hope that one day we can put all this behind us.

Defense: Thank you Joe. Nothing further, your honor.

(Counsel for the Defense is seated)

(Prosecutor stands)

Prosecution: Just one question, your honor.
Mr. Harlan, you say that Kristy
wanted you to use a condom. Was she
not using birth control?

Harlan: I... I don't know. I don't remember.

Prosecution: Well, now hold on. You said it
was her idea to use the condom. I am
guessing that if you talked about
condoms, you must have talked about
birth control. What did she say about
that?

Harlan: I really don't recall.

Prosecution: But, didn't you just testify,
and I quote – "I remember the whole
night. I remember everything?"

Harlan: Again, that conversation. It was kind
of heat of the moment. We used a
condom.

Prosecution: Nothing further, your Honor.

Judge: You may step down, Mr. Harlan.

(Joe Harlan Junior steps down)

Prosecution: Prosecution calls Kristy Wise to
the stand.

(Kristy Wise takes the stand)

Judge: Do you swear that the testimony you
are about to give will be truth, the
whole truth, and nothing but the
truth, so help you God?

Wise: I do.

Prosecution: Please state your name.

Wise: Kristy Wise.

Prosecution: Miss Wise. Are you attracted to
             Joe Harlan?

Wise: No.

Prosecution: Have you ever been?

Wise: No.

Prosecution: Prior to Halloween, had you spent
             any time alone with him?

Wise: No.

Prosecution: What do you remember about
             Halloween night?

Wise: It's a blur really. I remember
             getting dressed up to go out. I
             remember walking with Bethany to
             the party. I remember having a beer.
             And... And then I woke up in the
             hospital with my mom.

Prosecution: Do you remember Mr. Harlan at all
             from that night?

Wise: I remember he was there with Frank
             Stern. They got to the party a while
             after we did.

Prosecution: Did you speak to them?

Wise: Not that I can remember.

Prosecution: When you woke up in the hospital, what did you learn?

Wise: That I had Rohypnol in my system. And that he had sex with me. (Indicates the Defendant)

Prosecution: Do you recall consenting to have sex with Joe Harlan Junior?

Wise: Absolutely not.

Prosecution: Pass the witness.

Defense: (Stands) Miss Wise, Kristy, can I call you that? I only have a few questions - did you hear Joe speaking a few moments ago? Did you hear him explain his side of the story?

(Wise nods)

I'm sorry, but for the record, could you tell me if that's a yes or a no?

Wise: Yes.

Defense: And is there anything you would like to add to that? Anything you would like to say to him?

Wise: I... I did not ever want to have sex with you. I don't know if it was you or one of your friends that drugged me, but I hope you rot in hell!

Defense: Kristy. Do you remember not consenting to sex with my client, Joe Harlan?

Wise: Um, no.

Defense: Do you remember anything about
           Halloween night besides getting
           dressed to go out, walking to the
           party with your friend, Bethany, and
           drinking a beer?

Wise: No.

Defense: No further questions, your honor.

(Ms. Wise steps down)

Judge: Ms. Kraft?

Prosecution: The State rests, your honor.

Judge: Very well. Counselor?

Defense: We are ready to close, your honor.

Judge: Okay. Both parties having rested.
           Evidence is closed. We will now hear
           closing arguments. Fifteen minutes
           maximum to each side - including
           any rebuttal. We will begin with the
           State.

Prosecution: Ladies and gentlemen of the jury,
              this case comes down to one simple
              question: did Kristy Wise consent to
              having sex with Joe Harlan Jr.?

              There is no question that Joe Harlan
              had sex with Kristy Wise. Likewise,
              it is undisputed that she had been
              drugged, and that she had Rohypnol in
              her system.

The only problem here, as you've already heard, is that when given date rape drugs, the victim seldom remembers anything about the event. In fact, you've heard Kristy say that very thing, that she remembers nothing after leaving the party.

So, what do we know?

Mr. Harlan himself testified that the drug had been ingested by her more than twenty minutes before they had sex. Fifteen minutes to walk home. Ten minutes that he was "in the bathroom." She was under its influence.

The evidence shows that she sent uncharacteristic Tweets alluding to sex just before having sex, on a phone that oddly had no fingerprints on it whatsoever - all while Mr. Harlan was "in the bathroom." They had sex with a condom, but Mr. Harlan can't tell us anything about their discussion regarding birth control.

To convict Mr. Harlan, you must find it to be the case the he knew Kristy was in no condition to consent to sex. The physical evidence shows that she was drugged, the drugs were in her system, and she was incapacitated. The first witness on the scene - who came in while Mr. Harlan was still erect - found Kristy unconscious.

The State has proven that Mr. Harlan knew what he was doing. He knew that Kristy could not and did not consent to sex. He had his way with her.

Don't let him get away with it.

Defense: Reasonable doubt. What is reasonable? Two young people, on Halloween night, see each other at a party. They already know each other. They share common friends. Same university. They get to talking. They have a few drinks — maybe a few too many. They leave the party and go back to one of their apartments and they — two consenting adults — have protected sex. In this day and age, that is not hard to believe. That is not at all unreasonable, is it?

And maybe the next day, one of them regrets it. Or both. Perfectly understandable.

The only reason we are here today is because — to the perfectly reasonable scenario I just described, we must add one additional fact. Someone — and the evidence is clear it was not Joe — someone slipped Kristy a drug.

That is the guilty person!

That is the person who created this whole mess!

That is the person who should be on trial!

The evidence is clear that Joe did not drug Kristy.

The evidence is clear that Joe didn't even know about any drug.

The evidence is also clear that Kristy and Joe used a condom — this proves premeditation and not opportunism - consistent with two consenting adults who chose to have sex.

The State has failed to prove its case and that's because my client, Joe Harlan Junior, is innocent.

Ladies and gentlemen of the jury, in a moment you will leave the room to decide Joe's fate. And there is only one question that you have to answer — did Joe Harlan knowingly have sex with Kristy Wise without her consent?

We weren't there in that room. Only two people were. Only two people can tell us what happened.

That is the evidence you must rely upon.

One of those two people, Kristy, has stated very clearly that she does not remember not consenting to sex.

The other person, Joe, says that she did.

There is no evidence to the contrary.

Ladies and Gentlemen, I ask you — can
you imagine a scenario in that room,
any scenario, in which Joe understood
in his mind that Kristy consented to
make love?

If you can imagine such a scenario,
that is reasonable doubt, and you
must find Joe not guilty.

(Counsel for the Defense is seated)

Judge: Thank you all. Ladies and gentlemen
            of the jury, this case is now in your
            hands. You will now retire to the jury
            room for deliberations. The bailiff
            will provide you with your charge.

            The question you must answer, which
            the Defense correctly stated, is: Do
            you find, beyond a reasonable doubt,
            that Joe Harlan Junior knowingly had
            sex with Kristy Wise without her
            consent?

Bailiff: All rise.

(Jury Exits)

(Off the Record)

JURY TRIAL
July 13, 2016

BEFORE THE HONORABLE DAVID MORALES

(On the Record)

Bailiff: All rise.

(Jury enters and take their seats)

Judge: Please be seated everyone.

We have a question from the Jury.
Please hand me the... thank you,
Madame Bailiff.

Alright. So, the question reads as
follows: "Your Honor, if we are
unable to reach a unanimous verdict,
can we return a majority decision?"

Will the attorneys approach for a
short sidebar, please?

(Sidebar discussion was had off the Record)

Judge: Very well. Ladies and gentlemen of
the jury, I've spoken with counsel
regarding how best to respond to your
question. Counsel agree that I should
refer you to paragraph and six of the
Charge to the Jury which reads as
follows:

Paragraph six. Your answer must be
unanimous on each special issue. You
will not, therefore, enter into an
agreement to be bound by a majority
or any vote other than a unanimous

vote of all jurors on each special issue.

I know this may be a bit frustrating, but the law requires that the instructions to the jury be very specific, very precise. I will ask now that you please retire to continue deliberations in keeping with these instructions.

Okay?

The jury will now retire to continue deliberations.

Bailiff: All rise.

(Off the Record)

JURY TRIAL
July 14, 2016

BEFORE THE HONORABLE DAVID MORALES

(On the Record)

Bailiff: All rise.

(Jury enters and take their seats)

Judge: Please be seated. Ladies and gentlemen of the jury, have you reached a verdict?

Jury Foreman: (Stands) We have, your honor.

Judge: Is it a unanimous verdict?

Jury Foreman: It is.

Judge: Please hand me the Charge.

            Will the Defendant please rise?

(Defendant stands)

Judge: In the case of the State of Texas
            versus Joseph Harlan Junior, the jury
            finds the Defendant not guilty.

            Quiet please. Quiet.

Bailiff: We'll have order in the court. Order.

Judge: Mr. Harlan, you stand acquitted of
            the charges against you. You are free
            to go.

            Ladies and gentlemen of the jury,
            thank you for your time and effort in
            this case.

            We'll stand in recess.

Bailiff: All rise.

(Off the Record)

Austin, Texas
July 14, 2016.
The evening after the verdict.

It was golden hour in Tarrytown. An incandescent sun cast long shadows that pointed in unison toward nightfall. Birds sang. But their melodies were drowned out by crescendos of cicadas' chattering.

Not to be outdone, the wind came and went in gusts, rising up and across the hills from the lake below. As it did, it blew through the trees agitating the millions of leaves in the canopy, the rustle and crackle of which drew the eyes upward, where an infinite canvas of burnt orange and purple was visible through the branches of proud oaks.

All this beauty was lost on Kristy Wise.

She was running through the hills near her home.

Fast.

Her heart pounded. Arms pumped. She was at just under a seven-minute mile pace and running uphill. Fast, even for her.

Not sustainable.

But she didn't care. She was in her head. Remembering. Earlier that day, back in the courtroom. And all she could think about was *that look*.

The verdict had left her stunned.

Not Guilty.

The three syllables rang out from the judge's bench like gunshots, their muzzle blast burning Kristy's face, making her eyes water. As their sound ricocheted through the courtroom, it took on physical form—like toxic fumes poisoning the space between everything and everyone.

As the poison spread, Kristy sat motionless, in shock. Paralyzed. Unable to breathe. Sinking.

She'd suddenly sucked in air as she jumped to her feet, Bethany's restraining hand on her arm. Her mother had said something to her. Her father put his arm around her shoulders, strong, reassuring.

It took all her strength to walk, struggling to wade through the words—*Not Guilty*—pushing her way through them to leave the courtroom.

To just get out of there.

And that was when it happened.

Joe Harlan Junior was still by the defense table. His attorney was standing at his side, smiling. Hands in his pockets. Full of pride.

Harlan was hugging his father, who had his back to Kristy. The freshly-acquitted defendant was facing her, and as she made her way out, he saw her and turned his head slightly towards her over his father's shoulder. They locked eyes and his face remained somber, respectful, but a smile filled his eyes, only his eyes.

And the motherfucker winked.

It lasted half-a-second, maybe less.

It was then that Kristy had gone from stunned to furious.

She was barely able to contain her fury as she left the building and on the ride home. Her parents wanted to be there for her. To console her. But she needed to be alone with her rage.

Rage not just at *that look*, but also at the knowledge that she'd never get it out of her head. *That look* would haunt her. She would dream about it, she was sure.

She could see it as clearly as she could see the pavement she was pounding up Scenic Drive toward the top of the hill. She couldn't stop seeing it. No matter where she looked. Trees and a steep drop down to the lake on her left. Houses to her right. Hard black asphalt in front of her, under her feet.

That look wouldn't go away.

But it began to blur, as tears filled her eyes and streamed down her face. She tapped into her fury to drive *that look* away, increasing her pace, pumping her arms harder, gasping for air, sprinting up to the top of the hill. Trying to purge the image of Joe Harlan Junior winking at her from her memory.

As she reached the summit she choked, gagged, struggled to breathe, struggled to take in air.

There wasn't enough air.

Then, there was no air at all as bile rushed up her throat before spattering on the roadside.

* * *

"It's fucking bullshit, Tom! I don't give a rat's ass about excuses. Yours, that shit lawyer, or that goddamned jury. The bottom line is that little fucker got away with it!" Deb was pacing the kitchen and she was angry. Very angry. "Nothing else matters, Tom! Nothing!"

Tom had to give her credit. She'd held it together at the courthouse. She'd been cold but polite to the prosecutor, after which she'd marched, expressionless, past the media and the cameras. And she'd put on a supportive show for Kristy in the car.

But after Kristy told them that she was going out for a run, the moment her daughter closed the front door behind her, Deb exploded.

Tom was used to his wife's "communication style." They'd been married for almost twenty-five years. He had learned that sometimes she simply needed to vent, and when she did, she took no prisoners. It was something regarding which he'd once suggested anger management therapy. Once— after which she'd let him have it with both barrels, and the issue was never discussed again.

He knew he wasn't the target. Everything was. Shotgun style. It wasn't about him. It was just something that she needed to do.

He also knew that, once she was done, she'd return to rationality. Then they could discuss things logically.

At least, that's how things usually went.

This time it was different.

* * *

When Deb launched into her tirade that day, Tom had to admit that he agreed with pretty much everything she had to say. He couldn't understand the verdict either. He'd sat through the entire trial. He considered himself impartial, as much as anyone could be in his shoes. And he just couldn't fathom how those twelve people could *unanimously* agree that Harlan was not guilty.

He stood, arms folded, letting Deb's diatribe roll over him.

"Well, I'll tell you right now Thomas Kincaid Wise, I am done with the system! Fuck it! You hear me? Bunch of useless fuckin' paper pushers! I'm not putting her through that again," she said, pointing at him.

Deb was referring to the possibility of a civil suit against Harlan. There had been preliminary discussion about suing Harlan for damages. Of course, had he been found guilty, the suit would have been as close to a slam dunk as you could get.

But now, despite anything Deb did or did not want to do, that idea was practically dead. It wasn't a case of double jeopardy. Criminal liability and civil liability were two different things. But, a unanimous "not guilty" verdict applying the strict "beyond a reasonable doubt" criminal standard was likely to preclude a civil suit. It all "depended" to some degree, according to the lawyers—*res judicata* they'd called it—legal arguments could be made, but the odds were not good.

It wasn't a question of money. It never had been. It was a question of justice.

Tom had truly believed, until a few hours earlier, that as painful as the process was, his daughter would be vindicated. She would get the justice she deserved through the criminal court system. Deb had been doubtful, but for the sake of her baby girl she had gone along with the process, keeping her thoughts to herself.

That was over now.

It was a part of Deb's venting, to tell him what was going to happen and treat him as though he was advocating any and all other possibilities except what she was telling him was going to be done. He was fine with that. It was part of the process. It was all manageable.

Until Deb took things in a different direction.

"From the start, I told you! We should'a just handled this ourselves. You should've handled it the way my daddy would've." She paused, looking at Tom, and lowered her voice, "Just like Crockett."

She stopped the ranting and the pacing, and looked at him with folded arms of expectation.

Tom felt a chill run down his back and inadvertently swallowed hard.

Deb walked up to her husband and gave him a gentle kiss on the cheek before throwing her arms around him.

When the embrace was over, she stood back and held his gaze. "Like Crockett, Tommy," she said with a wry smile. "That's the way this needs to go. You need to be there. You need to be there for our little girl now." She poked him gently in the chest with her finger. "What goes around, comes around, Tommy. Don't you let me down." Then she paused and added, "Don't let Kristy down."

* * *

"Crockett" was an old family story.

Deb had grown up on a ranch. Tom had been there a few times, mostly to visit his mother-in-law, who had lived there until her passing. He had never met Deb's father.

The ranch wasn't as rustic or primitive as Deb made it sound when she described it, but it wasn't city living by any stretch either.

There were many tales about growing up on the ranch. Deb had shared them all, at the appropriate time. Repeatedly. Each had its own moral theme.

Life lessons according to Deb Wise.

Tom had heard about Crockett many times, as had Kristy. The story was that Deb's father—George, long ago deceased—had received several complaints from their neighbor—Arthur McCoy— that George's dog, a German Shepherd named Crockett, was getting onto the neighbor's property and harassing his chickens.

The chickens were well-cooped. No blood had been shed. But McCoy had warned George that that Crockett was "trespassing."

George's response to McCoy was that *his* Malinois was in heat. "Just keep the chickens cooped until it's over, Art, or spay the bitch," George told him.

Fair warning had been given on both sides. George may or may not have taken steps to keep Crockett contained. That part of the story was never clear.

But one morning, George was out on the front porch preparing for a day's work when Arthur McCoy pulled up in his beat-up old green pickup truck. He cautiously exited the vehicle and approached the porch.

Deb had just turned ten at the time. She remembered it clearly because she'd had her tenth birthday party that weekend. There was still confetti on the lawn. Even at that age, as McCoy walked around his truck, Deb could tell that he was carrying.

"George, I'm really sorry. But I found Crockett in my hen house. Three dead hens."

Her father met the man in the drive, and they shook hands.

Then, they both walked to the back of McCoy's pickup truck, and together unloaded a mid-sized brown tarp. They removed it from the truck bed—there was clearly something in it—and laid it on the ground. A few words were exchanged that Deb couldn't hear.

They shook hands again, and McCoy drove off.

Deb sat watching as her father went to the barn, then came back with a shovel.

"Come on, string bean," he said.

Deb followed him into the yard just behind their house, where he began digging.

After about ten minutes, Deb's mother stuck her head out the back door. She was drying her hands on her apron.

"Whatcha doin', George?" she asked.

"Crockett," was all her father said.

Deb's mother made a face, then spat, "That McCoy son-of-a-bitch," and went back in the house, the screen door slamming behind her.

It took twenty minutes for Deb's father to finish digging the hole—about three feet deep, four feet long, two feet wide. Deb remembered there was a light breeze, and she watched as stray pieces of confetti floated up and about, some ending up in the hole.

"Come on, string bean," he said again.

The two of them, father and daughter, went to the front of the house, then carried the tarp around back and laid it down just beside the hole.

Deb's father looked at her and said, "You wanna go inside?"

"No, daddy. I'm good."

George unrolled the tarp.

Deb remembered that at first, the dog looked fine. But when her father turned him, placing him in the hole, she saw that the right half of his face was missing. She immediately understood that the bullet had entered the left side of his head and exited the right.

George then buried his dog.

And that was where the story ended.

Usually.

Deb had told Tom this tale many times over the course of their marriage, the moral of the story usually being something about protection of private property or "good fences making good neighbors"—something like that. Deb always adapted the moral to fit the point she was trying to make.

But a couple of years back, Deb had expanded upon the story.

Tom recalled the date specifically because it was the night of his forty-fifth birthday—June 9, 2015—when Deb had "filled in the blanks." It was just a few months before Kristy's rape.

Tom and Deb were drinking that night. That in itself was unusual, even on a birthday. Tom had issues with alcohol. Nothing he couldn't control—he believed—sometimes he just had a few too many.

Deb didn't need to drink. She didn't really even like it much. But Tom had noticed a slight change in her back around that time. Wine with dinner. An after-dinner drink that she would normally have passed on. That particular night, they'd been drinking scotch on the back deck. Deb was "all in" with him for his birthday. She'd even bought cigarettes.

That was when she'd told him that Crockett's story hadn't ended with the handshake in the driveway and the burial.

There was more.

"After daddy put Crockett in his grave, I sat and watched him bury the poor animal. Putting dirt on top, filling the hole. Dirt and little bits of confetti. Lots of colors, but mostly white, like snow." She took a drag from her cigarette.

"As I sat there, I noticed that daddy's breathing and his shoveling were synchronized.

"Rhythmic, you know?"

Breath. Breath. Breath. Plop of dirt.
Breath. Breath. Plop of dirt.

"He paced himself, slowly filled the hole. As he did, and I listened, I realized that he wasn't simply breathing. He was saying something. He was speaking words.

"I inched closer, Tommy, straining to hear, until finally I could make it out. I understood what he was saying.

"*What. Goes. Around.*" Plop of dirt.
"*Comes. Around.*" Plop of dirt.
"*What. Goes. Around.*" Plop of dirt.
"*Comes. Around.*" Plop of dirt.

"I didn't think nothin' of it," she shrugged, "you know? I was just a kid." Deb looked at Tom. Her cigarette had burned out, about an inch of ash hanging off the end. Noticing, she dropped it in the ashtray and lit another.

She inhaled deeply, and as she exhaled, continued, "Then, about a month later—I remember 'cause it was Easter Sunday—I was getting dressed for church and I hear a truck pull up. Then a door slams. Then there's yellin'. So, I go to my window, stick my head out, lookin' down at the drive, and Arthur McCoy's green pickup is there, and he's yellin' at daddy and pointin'. And daddy's got his hands up like he's defending himself, like he didn't do nothin' wrong.

"And I hear him, McCoy, saying, 'It ain't right, George. It ain't right. That dog never did no harm to nobody.'

"And daddy keeps saying, 'Trespassing is trespassing, Art.'

"So, they go back and forth a bit, like that. Kinda circling each other. McCoy yellin' and daddy bein' reasonable, trying to calm him down.

"Then, finally, McCoy gets fed up and leaves. Slams the door to his truck, and skids out of there leaving a trail of dust.

"No handshake. Not this time.

"Well, I go on downstairs. And daddy's quiet. Calm. Having a cigarette. Like nothin' happened.

"Mom was ready for church. I remember she was wearing a pretty straw hat with a pink ribbon with her Easter dress. She put a bow in my hair from the same pink material, and she kissed my check. Then we got in her station wagon, the nice car, and we left the house for church.

"Well, you know the drive out of the ranch. It's not too long. Daddy was driving and mom was next to him. I was sitting in the back seat but leaning forward in the middle, right up between 'em. No seatbelts back then. I remember that mom and daddy were holding hands while he drove.

"Then, as we're getting to the gate of the ranch, I see that the gate's open. And I see old man McCoy in our front field. On our land. His pickup truck is stopped there, parked in the middle of the field by the big oak tree—you know—the one on the left when you're coming onto the property.

"And McCoy is standing there, in the bed of his pickup. He hears us coming, and he's watchin'. Like he's waiting for us, about thirty feet from where our gate is.

"He keeps standing, still as can be in the truck bed. And as we're getting up even with him, he turns his back to us. And he starts reaching up and struggling, trying to cut down his Malinois.

"The dog was hanging from the tree by a rope. By the neck, Tommy. Dead.

"And, I must'a made a noise, from the surprise of it or something, you know? 'Cuz daddy looks at me, flat, in the rearview mirror. Not happy, or sad, or mad. Just flat. And he asks me, 'What's that, string bean?'"

Deb paused. Her eyes were locked onto Tom's, but they were distant. She wasn't looking at him. She was looking at her father in her mind's eye. She took a swallow from her drink, then a deep drag on her cigarette, and blew the smoke out of the side of her mouth. Her lips formed the faintest beginnings of a smile as she continued.

"And I looked out at the dog, and McCoy trying to cradle her in one arm and cut the rope with t'other, and I said, 'What goes around, comes around, daddy.'

"And he just smiled. A wicked smile. And he nodded. And he kept on driving, turning left onto the road to the church."

PROLOGUE

When I try to piece together how this whole mess began, a part of me thinks it may have started over thirty years ago. At least the seeds were planted that far back, in the early 1980s. What happened then, at that summer camp in Texas, set the stage for everything that was to come.

Odd, how something so remote in time and geography continues to impact me here, today.

Sometimes I try to imagine her, how she felt—that eleven-year-old girl—as she ran, stumbling and tripping through the woods that night. I try to put myself in her shoes. When I do, I wonder if she was frightened.

Did she understand the consequences of what she'd gotten herself into? I imagine it felt otherworldly to her, like a dream. But not a good dream. No, one of the bad ones—the ones that make your heart machine-gun as you try to outrun some dark thing that's chasing you. But the faster you try to run, the slower you go, your legs feeling leaden, clumsy, useless. Panic sets in. Tears of frustration form. Fear takes hold and won't let go. You open your mouth to scream but realize, to your horror, that you're paralyzed. It's not that you can't scream; you can't even breathe. Not a dream—a nightmare.

Then again, all that may simply be my imagination. It could just be me projecting what I might have felt onto Joan.

Maybe she wasn't scared at all.

True, it was dark out. The night smelled of rain, but there was no lightning, only the far-off rumble of thunder hinting at a distant storm. There were no trail lights, no visibility but for the moon peeking out intermittently from behind a patchwork of clouds. But, Joan had been down this trail before. She was running toward the main cabin.

She had been at Camp Willow for almost two full weeks.

She had been up and down that trail at least ten times a day, every day. Of course, that was during the day, and always with her buddy, or a camp counselor (the children called them troop leaders).

Joan had never been on the trail at night. And never alone.

Maybe I imagine Joan was scared because, as an adult, I believe that she should have been. I would have been terrified.

Adults know that evil flourishes in the dark.

The woods aren't a safe place for a little girl to be alone during the day. But at night?

Any experienced hiker will tell you that the forest changes at night. Landmarks look different. Depth perception suffers, even in young eyes.

By day, a copse of crape myrtles to the side of a trail is obvious. The bright fuchsia flowers stand in stark contrast to the greys, browns, and greens of the surrounding trees and foliage.

Turning right at the crape myrtles leads you back to the main camp. If you miss the turn, the trail continues to wind down until it reaches the scenic overlook that drops fifty feet to the river and jagged rocks below.

By day, those fuchsia flowers would be impossible to miss. But at night that landmark would simply blend into the background.

You see, there are no pretty pink flowers in the woods at night.

By now, you're probably wondering what Joan was doing out alone in the middle of the night. What could make her leave the safety of her cabin without her buddy? And why was she running?

To answer that, I have to tell you a little bit about her first.

Joan was a cute, bright little girl. Those who didn't know her well might mistake her curious nature for precociousness. But she wasn't. In fact, she was respectful and responsible, as older sisters tend to be.

She was also one of those children who aren't afraid to speak their mind. That is how her parents had raised her. She came from one of those kinds of families where the parents speak to their children as though they are adults. And the kids do the same. No pussyfooting around.

Joan was clear about what she believed, too. She didn't scare easily.

She didn't start out scared that night. She started out curious. Sneaking around after lights-out. Snooping. She called it "spying."

It's natural in young children, this behavior. Visceral. Primordial. If you have children, you know what I'm talking about. Evolution has hardwired something into kids that says: *We must learn how to spy on others. How to gather "secret" information. How to stalk. We must learn to be predator, or we will become prey.*

It's a part of growing up. It's all fun and games.

But there is a stark line that divides games from reality.

Joan crossed that line as she approached the cabin she planned to spy on.

She knew these kids. She'd been watching them for the last couple of days, eavesdropping at lunch, that kind of thing. She'd overheard them talking, but she couldn't believe what they were planning was true.

If it was, she had to do something.

You see, Joan was raised with clearly defined notions of right and wrong. She went to Bible study. And Grandma had read to her, when Mom and Dad weren't around, from the Old Testament. About Satan and Original Sin. Grandma had taught her that there were certain things that were mystical, sacred, and dangerous. You just didn't play around with them.

Joan crept up quietly, purposefully between pools of light. Once she reached the cabin, she paused. She could hear voices. Even though it was well past lights out, there was definitely something going on in there.

Carefully, she raised herself just enough to see inside the screened window, then quickly lowered herself. She'd seen them—she wasn't sure if they could see her, if they were looking in her direction or not.

She listened closely, trying to make out what they were doing. But the only thing she could hear was the hammering of her heart against her ribcage, the ringing of the blood in her ears. She placed her hands over her mouth to silence the breath that was coming so quick and shallow that she was starting to feel giddy.

She slowly peeked in the window again, and saw that no one was looking in her direction. Her eyes had already adjusted to the dark. Even so, it took a few moments for her brain to register what was going on, and a few more seconds to actually understand what she was seeing.

Joan's mouth fell open. She couldn't believe what was happening, what they were doing. She gaped, involuntarily holding her breath, staring.

There were rules at Camp Willow. What campers could and couldn't do.

What Joan witnessed went way beyond breaking camp rules. She was shocked. Stunned. And she was angry. This wasn't just wrong. It was evil.

You'd go to hell for it.

She had to make it stop.

"I'm gonna tell!"

For one brief moment, everything froze. The woods went quiet.

The three words hung in the air.

A screech broke the silence, followed by the flapping of wings as a frightened creature of some sort flew from its roost. At the same moment, the kids in the cabin turned in unison and gawked at the source of the scream.

Joan looked at them. She knew them. As she looked from one to the other, and they stared at her, Joan realized that she was outnumbered.

She turned and fled as fast as her feet would carry her. As she did, she heard a girl's voice hiss in a loud whisper, "Joan, wait!"

Joan ignored her and ran away, toward the main cabin. She felt strong, energized, full of purpose. But as I told you before, the trail was dark. The moonlight came and went. A storm was brewing in the distance. There were strange noises all around her. Shadows formed menacing shapes along the path.

And Joan was alone.

They say that when accidents happen it is usually not any one thing that goes wrong, but rather, it is the cumulative effect of multiple failure modes. For little Joan, the adrenaline, the darkness, the disorientation, and the lack of depth perception—all of these factors—probably combined and led to a very bad outcome. This is what the sheriff later told Joan's parents.

Joan was lucky at first. Despite the odds, she didn't miss the turn on the trail. She didn't miss the crape myrtles. Joan took the correct path and was headed straight for the main cabin. Until she stumbled on a root and fell, hard.

Really hard.

Her knee smashed into the ground, taking the brunt of the fall. The impact knocked off her left shoe.

Joan started crying. Quietly, so no one could hear. She tried to collect herself and rolled up into a sitting position, rocking and holding her knee. Moving it gently. Assessing the damage.

A flash of lightning startled her, but also gave her enough light to see that her shoe was only a few feet away.

She tried to stop crying.

She wanted her mommy. Wanted to be home. She wished she hadn't been spying. Wished she hadn't seen what she'd seen.

But, she also felt deep down inside that everything would be okay. She knew that Jesus would protect her because she was a good girl.

The moon peeked out from behind the clouds. In the light, Joan crawled toward her shoe. As she did, through her tears, Joan saw movement.

Shadows taking human form.

They appeared, one at a time.

The kids she'd been spying on.

* * *

The following morning, the bugle sounded as it did every day at 8:30 a.m.

Joan's camp buddy, Ann, was an early riser and was up and ready for breakfast before most. She was surprised to find Joan's bed empty.

When the other girls in their cabin told her that they hadn't seen Joan, Ann started looking for her around the campsite. Eventually, exasperated and a little worried, she sought out their troop leader, Beth.

"Are you sure she isn't just messing around with you?"

Ann shrugged.

"Maybe she's in the bathroom?" Beth asked.

"Nope. I checked."

"I bet she went to breakfast early. It wouldn't be the first time. She's probably in the mess hall."

Ann shook her head. "I found this on the trail." She held up a blue Keds shoe—left foot.

"Ann, you're not supposed to leave the campsite alone. You know that."

"I know, but I was worried," the girl responded, looking down at the shoe in her hand.

Beth took the shoe from Ann and turned it in her hands. "Are you sure it's hers?"

"Nope," she replied, biting her lip, "but I think so. Pretty sure."

Beth thought for a moment, then said, "Give me a few minutes, and we'll go look for her together. Okay?"

Joan was not in her cabin or any of the others. She wasn't in the dining hall or anywhere else around camp. At this point, Beth advised the camp director that Joan was missing.

The camp director questioned Ann.

When Ann had gone to sleep at lights-out, Joan was in their cabin, in bed, where she was supposed to be. When Ann woke at the bugle call, Joan was gone. Her bed was mussed—it looked like it had been slept in, or at least lain in, but it was empty.

Ann had found the blue Keds shoe on the trail, past the crape myrtles, on the path to the main cabin. She even showed them the spot.

At the camp director's instruction, they performed another search of all cabins and the site.

No Joan.

This search had taken another hour, and it was at this point that Joan's absence became a serious concern.

Just before 10:00 a.m., the camp director called the sheriff's office. He and two deputies showed up shortly after and took control of the situation. The search for Joan began in earnest at 11:30 a.m.

At 1:00 p.m., the little girl's body was found at the edge of the river, broken on the rocks below the scenic overlook. It appeared that she had found her way to the edge of the canyon and fallen. She had suffered multiple broken bones, lacerations, and head trauma. Death would have been instantaneous.

Joan's family was notified. They immediately came to the camp, grief-stricken and withered.

The loss of a child is the ultimate tragedy. I cannot even begin to imagine how they must have felt upon receiving that devastating news.

The other parents, the lucky ones, were notified so that they could decide whether or not to come back early to retrieve their babies, many of whom were traumatized by the incident.

By the time Joan's body was taken away that evening, it was too late for the officers to do anything more. They agreed to return the next day.

That night at the camp, a service was held in Joan's memory for the counselors and children who remained.

The next morning, the sheriff and his deputies returned.

You will recall that this all happened almost thirty years ago. Way before the age of high-tech forensics, and long before CSI. It was a more innocent time. Simpler. The sheriff was an elected official—his main qualification for the job was his local popularity. His deputies were locals, too. Their training was minimal.

In a criminal investigation, one of the worst mistakes an investigator can make is allowing preconceived notions to taint the analysis. Unfortunately, that is precisely what happened here. The officers were pretty sure Joan had simply gotten turned around, probably lost her way, and fallen.

They still went through the motions, of course. They questioned the remaining children and the camp counselors, but learned nothing they hadn't already heard.

Suicide was discounted. Joan was a happy, well-adjusted child. None of the counselors reported any signs of depression or anything else. In fact, they remarked on the little girl's energy and personality.

Foul play was ruled out, as well. There were no signs of a struggle. Yes, there were other footprints up and down the trail leading to the overlook, but then, there would be. It was a very popular spot frequented by almost everyone at the camp.

Besides, what possible motive could anybody have to harm the little girl?

One deputy suggested the possibility of homicide to cover up another crime. But, what other crime? Joan had had nothing worth stealing. She'd been found fully dressed. She had not been molested in any way. The notion was discarded.

What made the most sense was that it had been an accident. Joan had gone out after hours, contrary to camp policy. She had been alone in the dark and become disoriented, taken a wrong turn, and fallen to her death.

It was a tragic accident. That's all. Nothing more and nothing less.

Everything was consistent with this theory, except for the fact that Ann had found Joan's shoe on the trail to the main cabin, and not on the way to the scenic overlook.

If Ann was right about where she'd found the shoe, it would mean that Joan had been on her way to the main camp, then lost her shoe, turned around, went back to the fork, headed for the ravine, and fell off a cliff to her death.

This simply wasn't logical. It made no sense.

The officers concluded that Ann was mistaken about where she'd found the shoe.

As one deputy put it, "Why in God's name would an eleven-year-old girl wander around in the woods, in the dark, in only one shoe?"

The case was closed.

The Talion Series

OUT NOW

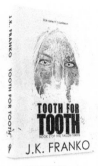

OUT 2020

OUT 2020

If you enjoyed

THE TRIAL OF JOE HARLAN JUNIOR

Please leave an Amazon review
so that others may enjoy it also.

To find out more about J.K. Franko, the Talion series and for access to exclusive additional content, register now at J.K.'s official website.

www.jkfranko.com